Key Stage 1

Maths Practice Papers

Hilary Koll and Steve Mills

Write your name in the box below before you start the practice papers.

Name

*After you have finished each test and had it marked,
your marks should go in these boxes.*

Paper 1: arithmetic	
Paper 2: reasoning	
Total	

Schofield & Sims

Contents

Note for adults helping with Paper 2: reasoning
The pull-out **Instructions for Paper 2: reasoning** should be removed from the book before the child starts Paper 2.

Schofield&Sims

Maths

Practice Papers
Key Stage 1

Maths

Practice Papers
Key Stage 1

Introduction

This book contains two practice papers. They will test your skills in maths. Use them to practise for the maths tests at the end of Year 2.

How to use the Key Stage 1 Maths Practice Papers

Ask an adult to help you decide when to do one of the practice papers. Ask them to keep that time free to help you. Do not look at either of the papers before then.

What you will need

Equipment:

- a dark pencil or a blue/black pen
- a rubber
- a ruler showing centimetres and millimetres (this may not be used in Paper 1)
- a clock or watch to time the tests.

Adult help:

- to read the pull-out instructions (found before the answer section)
- to make sure that you spend the right amount of time on each test
- to go through the practice questions before each test
- to mark each test when you have finished it.

Before you start

Read through the general instructions on page 5.

After a practice paper

Ask the adult to mark your practice paper.

If there were some questions that you found difficult, the Schofield & Sims **Key Stage 1 Maths Revision Guide** (available separately) can help you to revise these topics, using the page references given in the mark scheme.

Published by **Schofield & Sims Ltd**, 7 Mariner Court, Wakefield, West Yorkshire WF4 3FL, UK
Telephone 01484 607080
www.schofieldandsims.co.uk

This edition copyright © Schofield & Sims Ltd, 2016
First published in 2004
Second impression 2018

Authors: **Hilary Koll and Steve Mills**
Hilary Koll and Steve Mills have asserted their moral rights under the Copyright, Designs and Patents Act, 1988, to be identified as the authors of this work.

British Library Cataloguing in Publication Data
A catalogue record for this book is available from the British Library.

Designed by **Oxford Designers & Illustrators**
Printed in the UK by **Wyndeham Grange Ltd**
ISBN 978 07217 1362 5

General instructions

This book contains the following two practice papers.

- Paper 1: arithmetic (20 minutes)
- Paper 2: reasoning (35 minutes)

It is best to do the papers in the order they appear in the book, but don't do both the tests at the same time. Have a break between tests.

Before you start a test

When you are ready to do one of the practice papers, find a quiet place where you can concentrate.

Make sure you have enough time to complete the practice paper before you start it. The Key Stage 1 tests are not strictly timed but once started it is best to complete a test without stopping.

Ask an adult to help you get ready for the test. For Paper 2 they will need to read through the pull-out instructions (found before the answer section). Listen carefully and make sure you understand what to do. Ask questions if you are not sure.

When you are ready to begin, turn to the first page of the practice paper.

During the test

Work through Paper 1 on your own.

The first few questions of Paper 2 will be read out loud by the adult who is helping you. Read the other questions yourself and work through the rest of the test on your own. The adult will help you with difficult words.

Work through all the questions. Read the questions carefully and try your best to answer them all. Think carefully. If you can't answer a question, move to the next one – you can come back to it later. At the end, go back and check your work. If you need to do any working out, you can use any space on the page.

Stop at the end of the test. This is clearly marked 'End of test'.

Don't look at the answers before or during the test.

After the test

Ask an adult to mark your practice paper using the answers and mark scheme on pages 41 to 46. They should then write your total mark in the box on pages 3 and 47.

Look at any questions you couldn't do or answered incorrectly. These are topics you need to revise. The Schofield & Sims **Key Stage 1 Maths Revision Guide** will help you with this.

DO NOT TURN OVER THIS PAGE UNTIL YOU ARE READY TO START PAPER 1.

Paper 1: arithmetic

Practice question

This is a practice question.

Work out the answer and write it in the red box.

If you need to, use the space underneath for your working out.

$8 + 8 = $ ⬚

1 4 + 3 =

2 6 + 5 =

please turn over

3   17 − 7 =

4   26 + 10 =

5   19 − 5 =

6   16 + 2 + 3 =

7   57 – 4 = [ ]

8   37 + 6 = [ ]

9   43 − 27 =

10   78 − 30 =

please turn over

11 60 − 16 =

12 6 × 5 =

13 84 − 33 =

14 50 ÷ 10 =

15

$$\boxed{} + 4 = 9$$

16

$$\boxed{} + 7 = 26$$

17 $\frac{1}{2}$ of 26 = ☐

18 $\frac{3}{4}$ of 20 = ☐

please turn over

19 $73 - \boxed{} = 41$

20 $60 - \boxed{} = 20$

21 58 + 27 =

22 1 + 8 + 7 =

23 $\frac{1}{3}$ of 18 = [ ]

24 50 ÷ 5 = [ ]

25 $7 + 6 + 5 =$ ⬚

END OF TEST

**Total score for
Paper 1: arithmetic**
Write this score in the box
on pages 3 and 47.

Paper 2: reasoning

The practice question and the first five test questions will be read to you by an adult.

Practice question

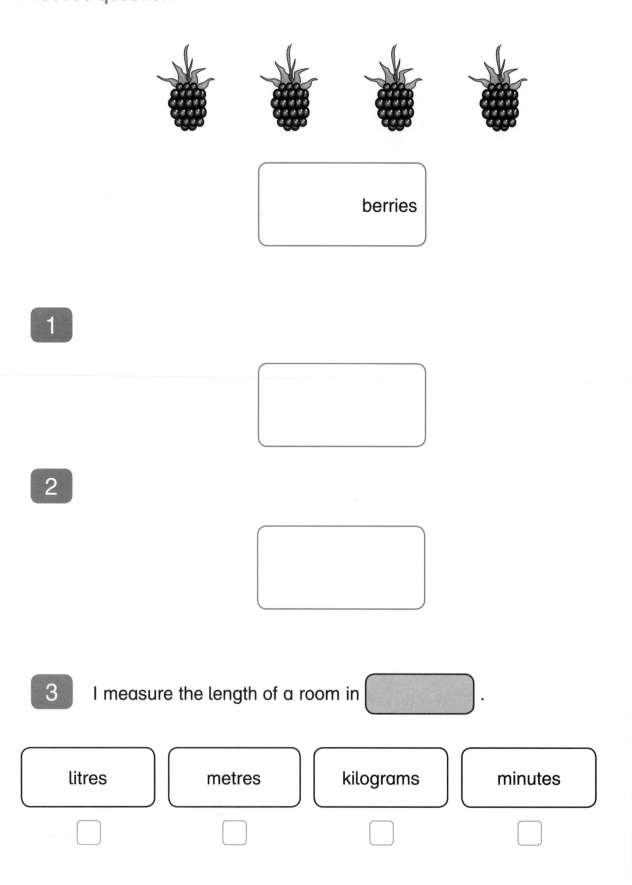

berries

1

2

3 I measure the length of a room in [   ] .

litres	metres	kilograms	minutes
☐	☐	☐	☐

4

5

days

DO NOT TURN OVER THIS PAGE UNTIL THE ADULT TELLS YOU TO.

6 Look at these cards.

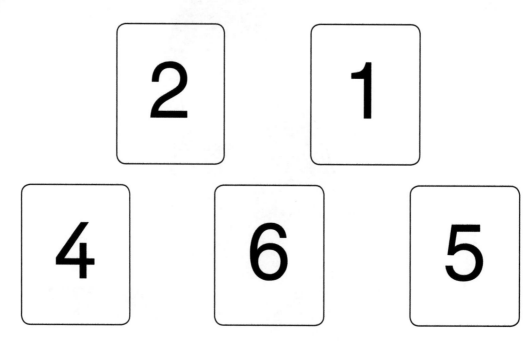

These two cards make a number **more than 60.**

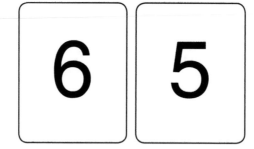

Pick two cards to make a number **less than 15.**

7   Write a number in the box to make this subtraction correct.

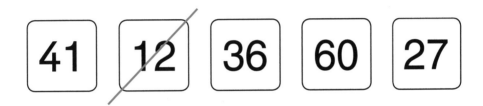

$$20 - 10 = 15 - \boxed{}$$

8   These numbers are not in order.

| 41 | ~~12~~ | 36 | 60 | 27 |

Write the numbers in order.

One has been done for you.

| 12 | | | | |

smallest   **largest**

9   This bar chart shows what some children like doing best on Saturday.

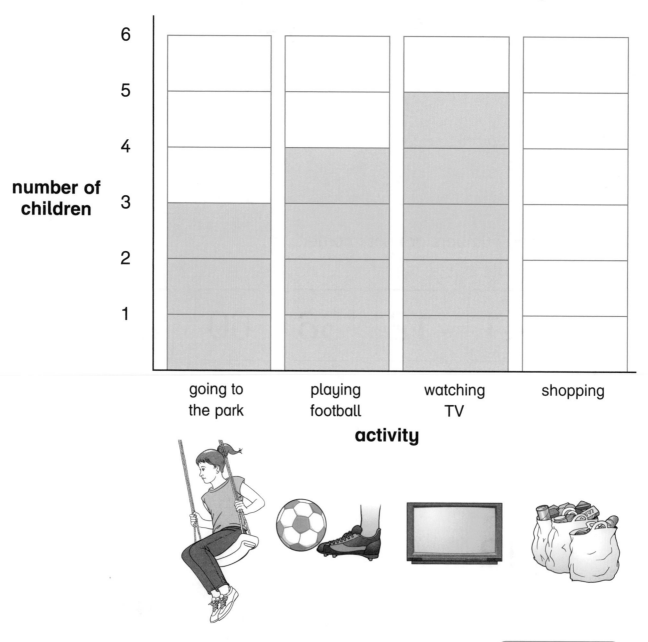

A bar chart to show children's favourite Saturday activities

number of children

6
5
4
3
2
1

going to the park   playing football   watching TV   shopping

activity

a) How many children like watching TV best?

b) **3** children like shopping best.

Show this on the bar chart.

10 Look at these odd and even numbers.

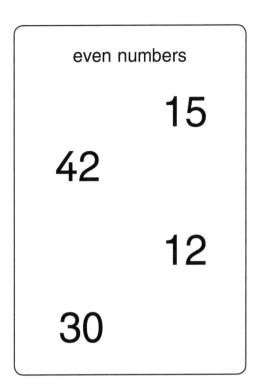

odd numbers	even numbers
17	15
31	42
25	12
23	30

Draw a ring around the number that is in the wrong place.

11 Fill in the missing numbers.

6   16   ☐   36   ☐

12 Jack eats half of these biscuits.

How many does he eat?

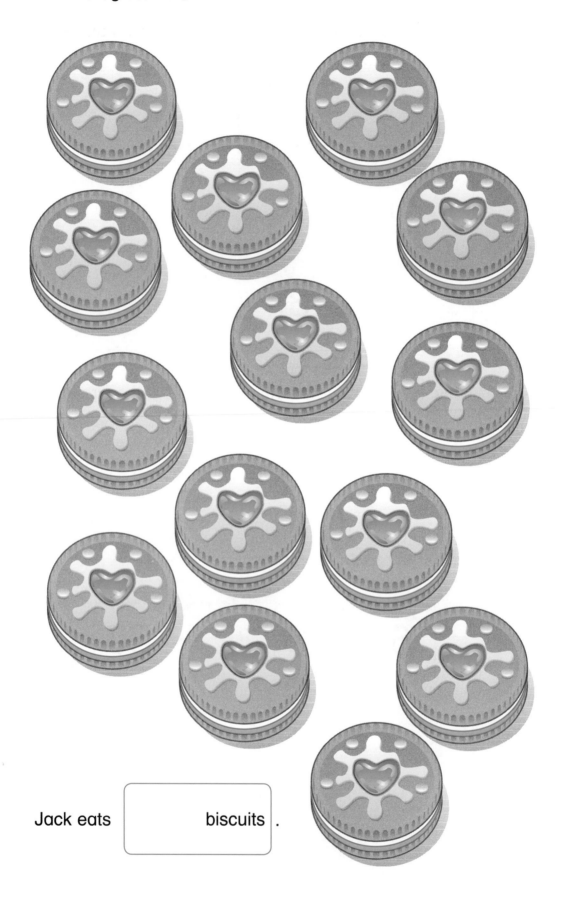

Jack eats ⬚ biscuits .

13 There are **10** sweets in each bag.

How many sweets are there altogether?

14 This shows the prices of some ice creams.

Strawberry 35p

Star 45p

Two scoops
55p

One scoop
40p

a) Which **two** ice creams together cost **exactly £1?**

and

b) How many **One scoop** ice creams
   can you buy for **exactly £2?**

15 Leah has these coins in her pocket.

a) How much money does she have?

p

She gives **25p** to her sister.

b) How much does Leah have now?

p

pages
28–29
total

please turn over

16   How much juice is in the jug?

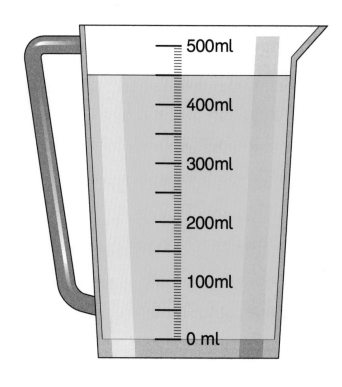

ml

17   Here is part of a number pattern.

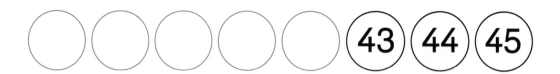

Where would **38** go?

Write **38** in the correct place.

18 Look at this **pictogram**.

Colours of sweets in a bag of Fruities

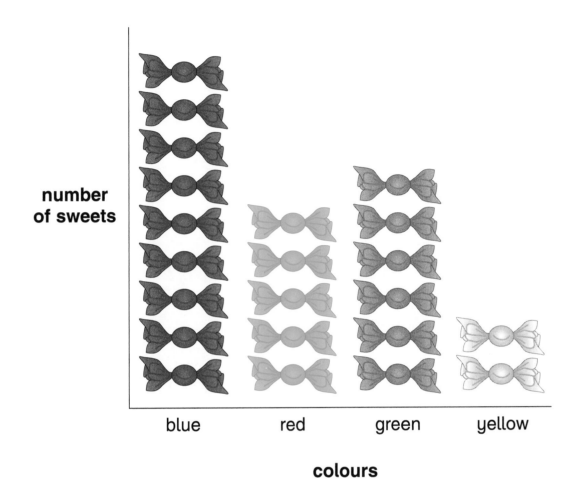

a) How many **green** sweets are in the bag?

b) How many sweets are in the bag altogether?

please turn over

19 Here are some sticks.

Draw a ring around the stick that is exactly **8cm** long.

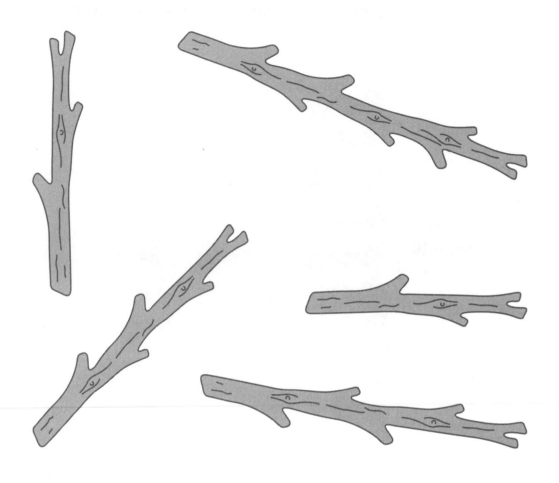

20 How much do these apples weigh?

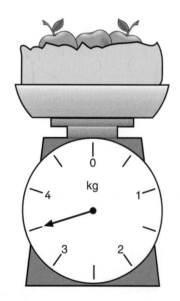

kg

21

Towers theme park

child   £4

adult   £7

How much does it cost for **3** adults and **2** children?

Show how you worked it out in the box below.

The cost for 3 adults
and 2 children is   £ _____ .

2 marks

pages
32–33
total

please turn over

22 Here are two hexagons.

Join some dots to draw a **different hexagon**.

Use a ruler.

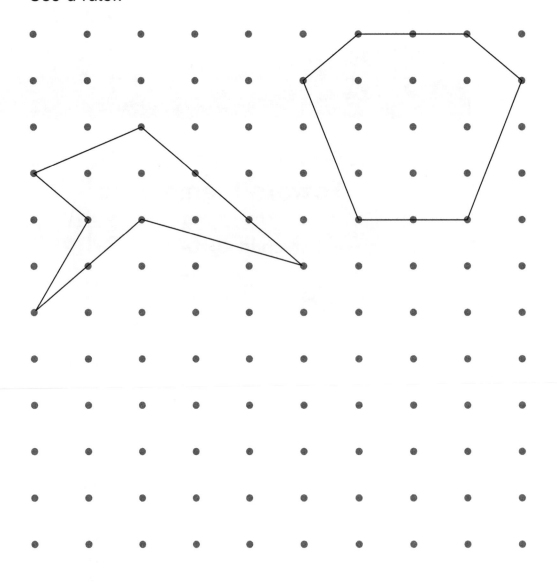

23 Complete this number pattern.

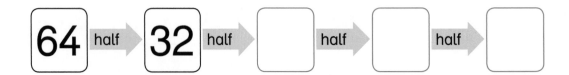

24

The coach sets off to London at this time.

It gets to London exactly 5 hours and 15 minutes later.

Show the time on this clock when the coach gets to London.

please turn over

pages
34–35
total

25 Look at this trail.

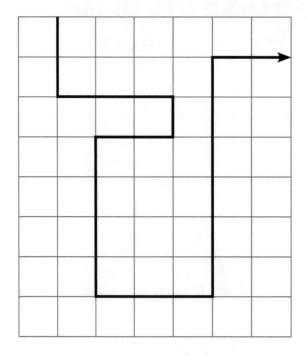

Complete these **instructions** for the trail.

down 2

right 3

down 1

[ ]

[ ]

[ ]

[ ]

[ ]

2 mar

26 What number do you think the down arrow is pointing to?

Write the number in the empty box.

27 Draw the reflection of this shape. Use a ruler.

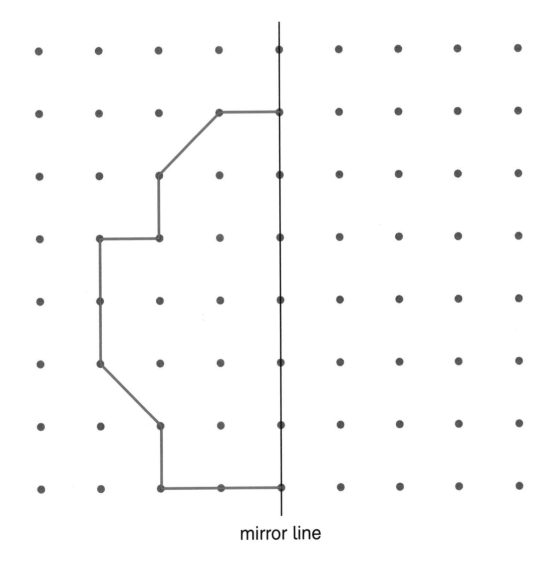

mirror line

28 Look at this pictogram.

Number of ice creams sold in one week

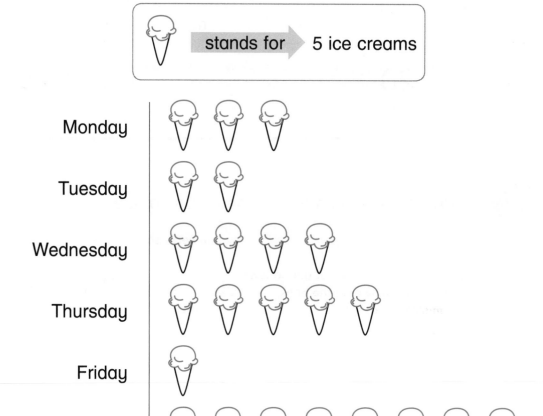

a) How many **more** ice creams were sold on Thursday than on Monday?

ice creams

b) **5** ice creams were sold on **Sunday**.

Show this on the chart.

END OF TEST

**Total score for
Paper 2: reasoning**
Write this score in the box
on pages 3 and 47.

Instructions for Paper 2: reasoning
(for adult helper)

Remove this page and read it before you talk to the child about doing Paper 2.

Start Paper 2 by reading out the practice question and the first five test questions (below) to the child. These five questions are referred to as the 'aural questions'. The child writes their answers on pages 20 and 21 before starting to answer the written questions (pages 22 to 38).

The tests are designed to help children to demonstrate their attainment. As a result the tests are not strictly timed, since the ability to work at pace is not part of the assessment. The reasoning paper is expected to take approximately 35 minutes.

Aural questions

Before you start

Read the following information to the child.
- **I am going to read out some questions for you to answer.**
- **I will read each question twice only, with a short gap in between.**
- **Listen very carefully to each question.**
- **You have plenty of time to work out your answer.**
- **You should write your answer in the book. I will tell you where on the page to write it.**
- **If you make a mistake, cross it out or rub it out. Then write your answer clearly.**

Ask the child to turn to page 20. Explain the following.
- **You write your answers in the red boxes.**
- **You can use any of the white space outside the boxes for your working out.**

During the test

Tell the child: **Now we are going to start the test.**

Read each of the questions below, saying the **bold** part twice, and leaving a short gap in between. Wait until the child has answered the question before you go on to the next one. Explain that the first question is a practice question. Help the child to locate each question if necessary.

P.	**Practice question**
	Look at the berries. How many berries are there?
	Write your answer in the box.
1.	**Question one**
	Add these three numbers: four and four and four.
	Write your answer in the box.
2.	**Question two**
	Write down an even number between forty-one and fifty-one.
	Write your answer in the box.
3.	**Question three**
	Look at the words in the boxes.
	The words say: litres metres kilograms minutes.
	One of the words completes this sentence:
	'I measure the length of a room in... '
	Tick the correct word.

continued overleaf

4.	**Question four**
	What number must Tom add to fifteen to get an answer of twenty-four?
	Write your answer in the box.
5.	**Question five**
	How many days are there in one week?
	Write your answer in the box.

As soon as the child has finished, explain that there are no more aural questions in the paper and introduce the written questions as described below.

Written questions

Before you start

Explain the following points to the child.
- **The rest of the questions are written down in the book.**
- **You have to read each question and work out the answer. Don't guess. Read what you have to do.**
- **You write your answer in the space in the book.**
- **Show your working out if you are asked to. You might get an extra mark for it. You can use any space on the page for your working out.**
- **If you make a mistake you can change your answer by rubbing or crossing it out.**
- **If you cannot do a question, leave it. Go back to it later if you can. Go on to the next question.**
- **Answer as many questions as possible.**
- **You have around 30 minutes to complete the rest of the paper.**
- **When you have finished, check your answers.**

During the test

Tell the child: **Now turn to page 22 and start the written questions.**

If the child is unable to read any unfamiliar words, you can provide help. However, you should not help the child with any numbers or symbols and you should not explain the questions.

As the test is not strictly timed, you should check that the child stops when they have done as much of the test as possible.

After the test

When the child has finished Paper 2, you can mark the test using the answers on pages 43 to 46.

Answers and mark scheme

Paper 1: arithmetic

Record the mark awarded for each question. Half marks cannot be awarded.

Question	Requirement	Marks	Additional comments	Revision Guide
Practice question	16	no mark		
1	7	1 mark	This question can be answered mentally or using a written method.	**Mental addition** pages 16–17
2	11	1 mark	This question can be answered mentally or using a written method.	**Mental addition** pages 16–17
3	10	1 mark	This question can be answered mentally or using a written method.	**Mental subtraction** pages 20–21
4	36	1 mark	This question can be answered mentally or using a written method.	**Mental addition** pages 16–17
5	14	1 mark	This question can be answered mentally or using a written method.	**Mental subtraction** pages 20–21
6	21	1 mark	This question can be answered mentally or using a written method.	**Mental addition** pages 16–17
7	53	1 mark	This question can be answered mentally or using a written method.	**Mental subtraction** pages 20–21
8	43	1 mark	This question can be answered mentally or using a written method.	**Mental addition** pages 16–17
9	16	1 mark	If using the standard written method of subtraction (sometimes known as decomposition), children will need to borrow 1 ten from the 4 tens so that 7 ones can be subtracted from 13 (rather than 3) ones.	**Written subtraction** pages 22–23
10	48	1 mark	This question can be answered mentally or using a written method.	**Mental subtraction** pages 20–21
11	44	1 mark	If using the standard written method of subtraction, children will need to borrow 1 ten from the 6 tens so that 6 ones can be subtracted from 10 (rather than 0) ones.	**Written subtraction** pages 22–23
12	30	1 mark	This question can be answered mentally or using a written method.	**Times tables facts** page 26
13	51	1 mark	This question can be answered mentally or using a written method.	**Written subtraction** pages 22–23

Question	Requirement	Marks	Additional comments	Revision Guide
14	5	1 mark	This question can be answered mentally or using a written method.	**Division facts** page 28
15	5	1 mark	If the child gave the answer 13, encourage them to notice that if 4 were added to 13 the answer would be 17, not 9. Point out that the missing number must be 4 *less* than 9, which can be found by subtracting 4 from 9.	**Mental addition and Mental subtraction** pages 16–17, 20–21
16	19	1 mark	If the child gave the answer 33, encourage them to notice that if 7 were added to 33 the answer would be 40, not 26. Point out that the missing number must be 7 *less* than 26, which can be found by subtracting 7 from 26.	**Mental addition and Mental subtraction** pages 16–17, 20–21
17	13	1 mark	Half can be found by dividing by 2.	**Finding fractions** page 30
18	15	1 mark	Three-quarters can be found by first dividing by 4 to find one-quarter and then multiplying by 3 to find three-quarters.	**Finding fractions** page 30
19	32	1 mark	This question can be answered mentally or using a written method.	**Written subtraction** pages 22–23
20	40	1 mark	This question can be answered mentally or using a written method.	**Mental subtraction** pages 20–21
21	85	1 mark	If using the standard written method of addition, children will need to carry 1 ten across from the ones as 8 + 7 = 15. This ten is then added to the 5 tens and 2 tens that are already in the tens column.	**Written addition** pages 18–19
22	16	1 mark	This question can be answered mentally or using a written method. Remind children that the numbers can be added in any order for addition.	**Mental addition** pages 16–17
23	6	1 mark	One third of a number is found by dividing it by 3.	**Finding fractions** page 30
24	10	1 mark	This question can be answered mentally or using a written method.	**Division facts** page 28
25	18	1 mark	Remind children that the numbers can be added in any order for addition.	**Mental addition** pages 16–17

Paper 2: reasoning

Record the mark awarded for each question. Half marks cannot be awarded.

Question	Requirement	Marks	Additional comments	Revision Guide
Practice question	4	no mark		
1	12	1 mark	If the child has written a digit in reverse, for example, the reflection of 2, they should be given the mark, provided that it clearly shows the characteristics of a 2 rather than a 5. If the digits are in the wrong order (for example, 21 rather than 12), do not give the mark. **This applies for all the questions in the tests.**	**Mental addition** pages 16–17
2	42, 44, 46, 48, *or* 50	1 mark	The child should be familiar with the term 'even number' and should know that the ones digit of an even number will be 0, 2, 4, 6 or 8.	**Odd and even numbers** page 5
3	metres	1 mark	If the child has circled, underlined or clearly indicated metres rather than ticking it, give the mark. If more than one word has been ticked, do not give the mark.	**Length** page 38
4	9	1 mark	A child hearing two numbers (in this case, 15 and 24) and an instruction will often add the numbers – which here would give an answer of 39. The child must be encouraged to listen to the question carefully. It can be answered using either counting on from 15 to 24 (addition) or counting back from 24 to 15 (subtraction).	**Mental addition** pages 16–17 **Mental subtraction** pages 20–21
5	7	1 mark		**Comparing lengths of time** page 43
6	12 *or* 14	1 mark	The child should notice that the only two-digit numbers less than 15 are 12 and 14. You can use similar number cards to make up similar questions for the child to practise.	**Numbers and digits** page 4
7	5	1 mark	A child sometimes sees the equals sign as an instruction to do something rather than as a sign of equality (i.e. that things on either side of it should be equal). As a result, the child may be confused that there is not simply an answer to the right of it. Show the child that 20 − 10 equals 10 and 15 − 5 also equals 10.	**Addition and subtraction facts** page 24

Question	Requirement	Marks	Additional comments	Revision Guide
8	27, 36, 41, 60	1 mark	If the child has answered this question incorrectly, they may not fully understand the value of digits in a number (tens and ones) – for example, that the 6 in 36 is worth less than the 6 in 60. Do not give a mark if the digits of any number are transposed or if any of the numbers are out of order.	**Ordering** pages 12–13
9	a 5	1 mark		**Block diagrams** page 59
	b bottom 3 rectangles shaded in the shopping column	1 mark	Give no mark if fewer or more rectangles are shaded.	
10	15	1 mark	Here the child must look to see which number is incorrectly placed in the Carroll diagram. A knowledge of odd and even numbers is necessary. Give the mark if the number 15 has been indicated in some other way, for example written at the side or ticked.	**Carroll diagrams** page 49 **Odd and even numbers** page 5
11	26, 46	1 mark	The child should notice that there is a pattern in the numbers given: they increase by 10. When counting on in tens, the ones digit always stays the same, for example 7, 17, 27, 37…	**Counting in tens** page 8 **Number patterns** page 15
12	7	1 mark	If the child has written a digit in reverse (for example, the reflection of 7), they should be given the mark, provided that it clearly shows the characteristics of a 7 rather than a 2.	**Fractions** pages 29–32
13	60	1 mark	The child should be using mental methods or using facts that they have learnt by heart to answer this question. It can be tackled by multiplication (6 lots of 10 or 6 × 10) or addition (counting on in tens).	**Mental addition** pages 16–17 **Multiplication** page 25 **Counting in tens** page 8
14	a Star and Two scoops	1 mark	The child may use trial and error for this question. To cut down the number of options, they may notice that the One scoop ice cream costs 40p and, when added to any other ice cream, will give an amount ending in 5p.	**Mental addition** pages 16–17 **Addition and subtraction facts** page 24
	b 5	1 mark	Encourage the child to explain to you how they worked out the answer to this question – for example, I added 40 five times, or I know that 4 × 5 = 20 so 40 × 5 = 200.	**Multiplication** page 25

Question	Requirement	Marks	Additional comments	Revision Guide
15	a 88p	1 mark	The total of all the coins is 88p. If the child experiences difficulty in recognising pictures of coins, they could place real coins onto the pictures and then count the coins.	**Money** pages 36–37
	b 63p	1 mark	Any method is acceptable for giving a mark, provided that the answer is correct – for example, counting back 25 from 88, subtracting 20 and then 5, counting up from 25 to 88, using a number line.	
16	450ml	1 mark		**Capacity** page 40
17	38 in the first circle	1 mark	The child needs to be able to count back from the numbers in the sequence. You can give them similar sequences for practice.	**Counting in ones** page 6 **Ordering** pages 12–13
18	a 6	1 mark		**Pictograms** page 58
	b 22	1 mark	The child should have added all the different colours together. $9 + 5 + 6 + 2 = 22$	
19		1 mark	Make sure that the child is using a ruler properly.	**Length** page 38
20	$3\frac{1}{2}$kg *or* 3.5kg	1 mark		**Mass** page 39
21	£29	max. 2 marks	Give 2 marks for the correct answer. Give 1 mark for correctly finding the cost for either 3 adults (£21) or 2 children (£8), and then attempting to add the two numbers.	**Multiplication** page 25 **Number problems** pages 34–35
22	any shape with 6 straight sides	1 mark	Give no mark if the shape has fewer or more than 6 straight sides.	**2-D shapes** pages 46–47
23	16, 8, 4	1 mark		**Number patterns** page 15
24	hands on the clock showing 4 o'clock	1 mark	Do not give the mark if both hands are identical in length.	**Telling the time** pages 44–45
25	left 2, down 4, right 3, up 6, right 2	max. 2 marks	Give only 1 mark if one of the instructions is incorrect. Give no mark if more than one instruction is incorrect.	**Positions** page 55 **Rotating** page 56

Question	Requirement	Marks	Additional comments	Revision Guide
26	28	1 mark	Split the line in half and then in half again to help the child estimate.	**Number lines** page 14
27		1 mark	If the child got this question wrong, use a mirror to show them the correct reflection.	**Symmetry** page 52
28	a 10	1 mark	The child needs to realise that one symbol on the chart stands for 5 items.	**Pictograms** page 58
	b 1 ice cream symbol drawn on chart by Sunday	1 mark	Again, the child needs to realise that one symbol on the chart stands for 5 items.	

Total marks

Ask the adult to write the total marks of both tests in the boxes below.

Paper 1: arithmetic (marks out of 25)

Paper 2: reasoning (marks out of 35)

Total marks (out of 60)

What your score means

Above 47 You are already achieving a good score and can do most of the things expected of you. There are still a few things you need to work on. Have a look at the questions you answered incorrectly. See if you can work out where you went wrong.

36–47 You can already do many of the things expected of you but there are still some key topics you need to work on. Look at the Revision Guide column on pages 41 to 46 for the questions you answered incorrectly. This will show you the things you need to revise.

Below 36 You can do some of the things expected of you but there are still a number of topics you need to work on to help you prepare for the test. Ask an adult to help you revise the topics that you found difficult.

Revision Guide

The Schofield & Sims **Key Stage 1 Maths Revision Guide** can help you with revising the things you need to work on. It covers all of the number, measurement, geometry and statistics topics and also includes Test Yourself questions to give you further practice. A helpful glossary allows you to look up any words that you didn't understand in the practice papers.

Schofield&Sims

the long-established educational publisher specialising in maths, English and science

The **Key Stage 1 Maths Practice Papers** contained in this book reflect the appearance and content of the national tests at Key Stage 1. Papers on arithmetic and mathematical reasoning are included, as well as full instructions and detailed mark schemes. Cross-references to the separate **Key Stage 1 Maths Revision Guide** allow children and adult helpers to tailor revision for exam success.

The Schofield & Sims **Practice Papers** are closely matched to the National Curriculum test frameworks and help children to revise what they have learnt at school, in preparation for the end of key stage tests. Detailed instructions on using the papers, and guidance on equipment and timings, provide reassurance and help children to become familiar with a more formal test situation.

Five Schofield & Sims **Practice Papers** books are available, providing rigorous practice in maths and English at Key Stages 1 and 2, as well as science at Key Stage 2.

The **Practice Papers** feature:
- formal exam-style questions, similar to those found in the national tests
- comprehensive instructions for both the child and adult helper
- a clear mark scheme with additional comments and guidance
- cross-references to relevant information in the corresponding revision guide.

Key Stage 1 Maths
Revision Guide
ISBN 978 07217 1360 1

Key Stage 1 English
Revision Guide
ISBN 978 07217 1364 9

Key Stage 1 Science
Revision Guide
ISBN 978 07217 1368 7

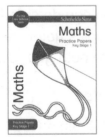

Key Stage 1 Maths
Practice Papers
ISBN 978 07217 1362 5

Key Stage 1 English
Practice Papers
ISBN 978 07217 1366 3

ISBN 978-07217-1362-5

MIX
Paper from responsible sources
FSC® C010219
www.fsc.org

For further information and to place your order visit
www.schofieldandsims.co.uk or telephone 01484 607080

ISBN 978 07217 1362 5
Key Stage 1
Age range 5–7 years
£3.95 (Retail price)